JOHANN CHRISTIAN BACH

SYMPH

D major/D-Dur/Ré majeur
Op. 18/4

Edited by/Herausgegeben von
Alfred Einstein

Ernst Eulenburg Ltd

London · Mainz · Madrid · New York · Paris · Tokyo · Toronto · Zürich

JOHANN CHRISTIAN BACH
SINFONIA D MAJOR, OP. 18 N̊ 4

"Mr. Bach from London has been here a fortnight; he is going to write a French opera,... his delight and my delight, on meeting again, you can easily imagine—perhaps his delight is not so true—but one must admit that he is an honest man and does people justice; I love him (as you may know) with all my heart—and have reverence for him..."

That is Mozart's judgment of Johann Christian Bach; he writes it, during his stay in Paris, on August 27th, 1778 to Leopold Mozart. And the love and reverence to which Mozart here confesses applies to the human as well as to the artistic personality of Johann Christian Bach. The personal acquaintance of the two dates back to Mozart's earliest years, to the first journey to London in April 1764, when the child prodigy received the most affectionate furtherance through Bach. With the feeling of gratitude to the noble and unenvious man is combined that of obligation towards an admired and profoundly congenial exemplar. At the age of ten, Mozart rewrites three of Bach's piano sonatas as piano concertos and furnishes them with cadenzas (Köchel No. 107); the recollection of Bach's music accompanies him up to his years of maturity; in all these years in which ever changing impressions are at work upon the creation of the "Mozart style" it is a constant "dominant". Mozart's letters are full of mentions of Bach, and

Mozart's works prove that he occupied himself again and again with Bach's music. No higher praise can be bestowed on Johann Christian Bach.

*

Johann Christian Bach, the so-called Milanese or London (English) Bach, born in Leipzig on Sept. 5th, 1735, was the youngest son of the great Sebastian, and his favourite: in his lifetime the father presented him with "3 claviers with pedal"—an act to which, according to the inventory of J. Sebastian's property, the children by the first wife—Wilhelm Friedemann, Carl Philipp Emanuel, and the maiden Catharina Dorothea—strongly objected. (But previously the two eldest sons had "reduced the estate by annexing the entire stock of *musicalia*"...). At the death of the father Johann Christian was fifteen years old; he becomes clavier pupil of Philipp Emanuel in Berlin or Potsdam, but in 1754 or 1756 resolves to go to Italy,—as the first of the Bach family acutely to feel the craving for the South and to yield to it. As private *capellmeister* to Count Agostino Litta in Milan, he also becomes a pupil of the famous Padre Martini in Bologna for composition, begins with church-music and is interested in Palestrina; but he is far more deeply impressed by the operas of the Neapolitan masters (1757 he is in Naples) and

II

the symphonies of Sammartini the Milanese... 1760 he becomes — having mean-
while gone over to the Catholic Church —
organist of Milan cathedral, writes a year
later, for Turin and Naples, his first operas
("Artaserse", "Catone in Utica") which
are followed in 1762 by "Alessandro
nelle Indie" for Naples, and in the
summer of this year he finds his way to
London via Mecklenburg-Strelitz, because
in 1761 Princess Sophie Charlotte of
Mecklenburg-Strelitz had become the
wife of the King of England. Until the
end of his life he remains music-master
of the Queen. He writes more or less
successful operas: 1763 "Orione" and
"Zanaida", 1765 "Adriano in Siria",
1767 "Carattaco", 1772 and 1776 (for
Mannheim) "Temistocle" and "Lucio
Silla" — the same libretto which the
young Mozart also composed — 1778 "La
Clemenza di Scipione", 1779 "Amadis des
Gaules" (for Paris). Some arias from these
operas fascinate the entire contemporary
world, from London to Petersburg, from
Naples to Copenhagen. He writes oratorios,
church-music, canzonettas, *piano*-sona-
tas, chamber-music of almost every kind,
concertos. On February 29th, 1764 he
begins together with his friend, the viola
da gamba player and composer Carl
Friedrich Abel (of whom a symphony
has hitherto circulated under Mozart's
name), the famous Bach-Abel concerts
which soon became a centre of London
concert life. He conceives a deep love for
the beautiful Auguste Wendling, daughter
of the Mannheim flautist, who however
prefers to remain one of the mistresses
of the Elector Carl Theodor... 1773 he

marries the less beautiful, but sym-
pathetic Italian singer, Cecilia Grassi
(here also a parallel to Mozart — Aloisia
Weber and Constanze...). He dies on
January 1st, 1782 leaving debts to the
amount of £ 4,000 sterling; and a few
days later just four friends follow the coffin
to St. Pancras. I derive these particulars
from the biography of J. Chr. Bach
published by Ch. S. Terry 1929 (London,
Oxford University Press), which is very
soon to appear in a German edition
(Leipzig, Breitkopf & Härtel).

*

From the many symphonies of J. Chr.
Bach preserved in prints and manus-
cripts — there are more than sixty — we
have chosen, to begin with, a D major
symphony contained as number four, in
Bach's last work, Op. XVIII, said to have
been published 1781. It includes three
symphonies for double orchestra — which
represent an older, concerto-like type
of symphony — and three for ordinary,
"modern" orchestra; two of the concerto-like symphonies (Op. 18,1 E-flat
major and Op. 18,3 D major) and a B-flat
major symphony (identical with the overture for "Lucio Silla") have already been
published by Fritz Stein (ed. Peters). With
the original edition, in which the trumpet
and timpani parts are missing, I have
compared the reprint (?) of the Amster-
dam publisher J. Schmitt, an edition
which contains under the same opus
number XVIII, besides another D major
symphony, ours as well. Both copies
vie with each other as regards in-
correctness; but by combining and

supplementing all the data, it is possible to establish the original articulation and gradation of tone with some degree of certainty. The Andante occurs in different, richer, orchestration (with three "Clarinetti d'amore") in the symphony of the Darmstadt copy of "Temistocle" (1772), but for us the concert version of the movement must remain decisive. The oboe parts bear the inscription "Oboe ò flauto" — "Oboes or Flutes". But the flutes in the first and last movements would be far from effective owing to the low range of their parts. A suspicion that the trumpets and drums may have been added in Schmitt's edition is not too far-fetched.

The figured bass-part in Schmitt's edition merely points to the practice kept up in London longer than elsewhere of directing even pure symphony-music from the cembalo — even Haydn, during his first visit to England, still had to conform to this custom. The cembalo would only burden this winged symphony; thus, the original engraved edition no longer has any figuring. The appoggiatura ornaments have been retained according to the original, and not interpreted "as understood by the modern practice". Even to-day there is no complete clearness with regard to this interpretation, and perhaps there never will be. But it goes without saying that in the first movement of our symphony, bar 8, the small notes are real, or (as Ph. Em. Bach terms them) "short" appoggiaturas "of unvarying duration"; that on the other hand, as for instance, in bar 27 of the Andante, the appoggiatura must be "broken up", the first quaver

consisting of four demisemiquavers. But whether in bar 54 and 58 of the first movement the little grace-note takes away, a minim, or even a dotted minim, from the principal note cannot be definitely decided even according to the contemporary text-books. All these questions must be settled individually and by everyone for himself according to his own knowledge and taste. My best thanks are due to my friend Dr. Ludwig Landshoff in Berlin, whose knowledge of all that concerns Johann Christian Bach is unsurpassed, for his counsel; I am also indebted to Professor Dr. Friedrich Noack of Darmstadt for information kindly given.

*

Our symphony is, to some extent, a "French" symphony (of course by no means a "French Overture" in the proper sense of the word), but a sinfonia in the French taste, quite similar to that composed by Mozart in 1778 for the *Concert spirituel*, with which it also shares the key. That, too, begins with the "premier coup d'archet" of which Johann Christian was always very fond, and works up a commonplace theme without much complexity to the fortissimo on the dominant — it is as if a splendid portal were being opened with festive pomp — the 2nd violins even contribute a few French roulades. A dainty second theme appears which leads back, with a quite Mozart-like turn, into the region of the chief *motif* — which now suddenly loses its commonplace character and reveals its deeper quality. We find ourselves in a development without noticing it, everything is of a surprising homogeneity and variety. One must not yet expect a "discursive" exposition of the themes in the Haydn manner; a Bach sinfonia is not the principal piece of a concert-evening, but introduction, conclusion, intermezzo: it must not transgress certain limits of sentiment and emphasis. Thus the cloudy shadows which here and there darken the pastoral landscape of the second movement are not threatening, and quite French and cheerful is the finishing Rondo with its two dainty "couplets" and the ingeniously summarising Coda. But all in all: what freshness of invention, what abundance of wit! This symphony was a work for real "connoisseurs". They doubtless knew how to appreciate it when in the middle part of the first movement, which we dared not call a development, the *cantabile* theme appears, not ingratiating but loud and sforzando; they will have enjoyed it when in the *reprise* the entry of the second theme is not so smoothly attained as the first time, but in a rather threatening, roundabout way (bar 104 seq.); the interplay of the instruments in the crescendo of the Coda (bar 140 seq.) will have struck them as being new and attractive. This symphony reflects only a part of Johann Christian Bach's musical personality: only his wit, his amiability, his cheerfulness, not the peculiar strong and delicate sensuousness which his nature had absorbed in Italy. But even with this restriction it is something rounded and entire.

Alfred Einstein

JOHANN CHRISTIAN BACH
SINFONIA D DUR, OP. 18 N⁰ 4

„Mr. Bach von London ist schon 14 Tage hier, er wird eine französische *Opera* schreiben ... seine Freude, und meine Freude als wir uns wieder sahen, können Sie sich leicht vorstellen — vielleicht ist seine Freude nicht so wahrhaft — doch man muß ihm dieses lassen, daß er ein ehrlicher Mann ist, und den Leuten Gerechtigkeit widerfahren läßt; ich liebe ihn (wie Sie wohl wissen) von ganzem Herzen — und habe Hochachtung für ihn ...‟ Das ist Mozarts Urteil über Johann Christian Bach; er schreibt es, während seines Pariser Aufenthalts, am 27. August 1778, an Leopold Mozart. Und die Liebe und Hochachtung, die Mozart hier bekennt, gilt sowohl der menschlichen wie der künstlerischen Persönlichkeit Johann Christian Bachs. Die persönliche Bekanntschaft beider geht zurück auf die frühesten Jahre Mozarts, auf den Londoner Aufenthalt vom April 1764, da das Wunderkind durch Bach die liebreichste Förderung erfährt. Mit dem Gefühl der Dankbarkeit für den noblen und neidlosen Menschen verbindet sich das der Verpflichtung an ein bewundertes und im Tiefsten wesensverwandtes Vorbild. Als Zehnjähriger arbeitet Mozart drei Klaviersonaten Bachs zu Klavierkonzerten um und versieht sie mit Kadenzen (Köchel Nr. 107); die Erinnerung an Bachs Musik begleitet ihn bis in die Jahre seiner Reife, sie ist in all diesen Jahren, in denen immer wechselnde Eindrücke an der Bildung des „Mozartschen Stils‟ wirken und schaffen, eine bleibende Dominante. Mozarts Briefe sind voll von Erwähnungen Bachs, und Mozarts Werke bestätigen, daß er sich immer wieder mit Bachscher Musik beschäftigt hat. Man kann zur Ehre Johann Christian Bachs nichts Höheres und Rühmlicheres sagen.

*

Johann Christian Bach, der sogenannte Mailänder oder Londoner (englische) Bach, geboren in Leipzig am 5. September 1735, war der jüngste Sohn des großen Sebastian und sein Liebling: noch zu Lebzeiten schenkt ihm der Vater „3 Clavire nebst Pedal‟ — ein Akt, der laut Bestands-Aufnahme des J. Sebastianschen Nachlasses von den Kindern erster Ehe — Wilhelm Friedemann, Carl Philipp Emanuel und Jungfrau Catharina Dorothea Bachin — höchlichst beanstandet wird. (Vorher aber haben die beiden ältesten Söhne den Nachlaß „um den ganzen Musikalienbestand geschmälert‟ ...) Beim Tod des Vaters war Johann Christian fünfzehn Jahre alt; er wird Klavierschüler Philipp Emanuels in Berlin oder Potsdam, faßt aber 1754 oder 1756 den Entschluß, nach Italien zu gehen — als erster des Bachschen Geschlechts, der diesen Drang nach dem Süden heftig fühlt und ihm nachgibt. Er wird, als

Hauskapellmeister des Grafen Agostino Litta in Mailand, noch Kompositionsschüler des berühmten Padre Martini in Bologna, beginnt mit Kirchenmusik und interessiert sich für Palestrina; viel tiefer aber wirken auf ihn die Opern der neapolitanischen Meister (1757 ist er in Neapel) und die Sinfonien des Mailänders Sammartini... 1760 wird er — er ist inzwischen zum Katholizismus übergetreten — Organist am Mailänder Dom, schreibt ein Jahr später für Turin und Neapel seine ersten Opern („Artaserse", „Catone in Utica"), denen 1762 für Neapel „Alessandro nelle Indie" folgt, und findet im Sommer dieses Jahres auf dem Umweg über Mecklenburg-Strelitz den Weg nach London — denn 1761 war die Prinzessin Sophie Charlotte von Mecklenburg-Strelitz die Gattin des Königs von England geworden. Bis ans Ende seines Lebens bleibt er Musikmeister der Königin. Er schreibt mehr oder minder erfolgreiche Opern: 1763 „Orione" und „Zanaida", 1765 „Adriano in Siria", 1767 „Carrattaco", 1772 und 1776 für Mannheim „Temistocle" und „Lucio Silla" — dasselbe Textbuch, das auch der junge Mozart komponiert hat —, 1778 „La Clemenza di Scipione", 1779 für Paris „Amadis des Gaules". Manche Arien aus diesen Opern bezaubern die ganze Epoche, von London bis Petersburg, von Neapel bis Kopenhagen. Er schreibt Oratorien, Kirchenmusik, Canzonetten, Klaviersonaten, Kammermusik fast jeder Art, Konzerte. Am 29. Februar 1764 beginnt er mit seinem Freunde, dem Gambisten und Komponisten Carl Friedrich Abel (von dem eine Sinfonie bisher unter Mozarts Namen ging) die berühmten Bach-Abel-Konzerte, die bald ein Mittelpunkt des Londoner Konzertlebens werden. Eine tiefe Liebe faßt er zu Auguste Wendling, der schönen Tochter des Mannheimer Flötisten, die aber vorzieht, eine der Maitressen des Kurfürsten Carl Theodor zu bleiben. 1773 heiratet er eine weniger schöne, aber sympathische italienische Sängerin, Cecilia Grassi (auch hier eine Parallele zum Falle Mozart — Aloisia Weber — Constanze...). Am 1. Januar 1782 stirbt er — mit Hinterlassung von 4000 Pfund Schulden; und ein paar Tage später folgen ganze vier Freunde dem Sarg nach St. Pancras. Ich entnehme diese Angaben der Biographie J. Chr. Bachs, die Ch. S. Terry 1929 veröffentlicht hat (London, Oxford University Press) und die sehr bald auch in deutscher Bearbeitung (Leipzig, Breitkopf & Härtel) vorliegen wird.

*

Aus den vielen gedruckten und handschriftlich erhaltenen Sinfonien J. Ch. Bachs — es sind über sechzig — haben wir zunächst eine D dur-Sinfonie ausgewählt, die als Nummer vier in Bachs vermutlich 1781 erschienenem letzten Werk, op. XVIII, enthalten ist. Es umfaßt drei Sinfonien für Doppelorchester — die einen älteren, konzertanten Typ der Sinfonie vertreten — und drei für einfaches, „modernes" Orchester; zwei der konzertanten Sinfonien (op. 18,1 Es dur und op. 18,3 D dur) und eine B dur-Sinfonia (identisch mit der Ouvertüre zum

„Lucio Silla") sind bereits von Fritz Stein bei Peters herausgegeben worden. Mit dem Originaldruck, dem die Stimmen der Trompeten und der Pauke fehlen, habe ich den Nachdruck (?) des Amsterdamer Verlegers J. Schmitt verglichen, eine Ausgabe, die unter der gleichen Opusnummer XVIII neben einer andern D dur-Sinfonie auch die unsere enthält. Beide Vorlagen wetteifern miteinander an Inkorrektheit, wenn auch der Originaldruck den Vorzug verdient; doch läßt sich durch Kombinierung und Ergänzung aller Angaben die originale Artikulation und Dynamik mit einiger Sicherheit feststellen. Das Andante findet sich in anderer, reicherer Besetzung — mit drei „Clarinetti d'amore" — in der *Sinfonia* des Darmstädter Exemplars des „Temistocle" (1772), doch muß für uns die Konzertfassung des Satzes maßgebend bleiben. Die Oboenstimmen tragen die Aufschrift „Oboe ò flauto" — „Oboen oder Flöten" — die zu tiefliegenden Flöten in den Ecksätzen würden jedoch wenig Wirkung tun. Nicht ganz ferne liegt auch der Verdacht, Trompeten und Pauken könnten Zusatz der Schmitt'schen Ausgabe sein.

Die Bezifferung der Baßstimme in Schmitts Ausgabe weist lediglich hin auf die in London sich länger als anderwärts erhaltende Gepflogenheit, auch reine Sinfonik vom Cembalo aus zu dirigieren — noch Haydn während seines ersten englischen Aufenthalts muß sich ja dieser Gepflogenheit fügen. Das Cembalo würde diese beflügelte Sinfonie nur belasten; so hat denn auch der Originaldruck keine Bezifferung mehr. Die Vorschlagsmanieren sind nach dem Original bei-

behalten und nicht etwa „im Sinn der heutigen Praxis" ausgedeutet worden. Über diese Ausdeutung besteht auch heute noch nicht volle Klarheit, und wird vielleicht nie volle Klarheit bestehen. Es versteht sich zwar von selbst, daß im 1. Satz unserer Sinfonie Takt 8 die kleinen Noten richtige, oder, nach Ph. Em. Bachs Bezeichnung, „unveränderliche kurze" Vorschläge sind, daß dagegen etwa in Takt 27 des Andante der Vorschlag „aufzulösen" ist, das erste Achtel also aus vier Zweiunddreißigsteln besteht. Aber ob in Takt 54 und 58 des ersten Satzes die kleine Vorschlagsnote von der Hauptnote eine halbe Note oder gar eine punktierte Halbe wegnimmt, ist auch nach den zeitgenössischen Lehrbüchern nicht völlig eindeutig zu entscheiden. All diese Fragen müssen im einzelnen und von jedem einzelnen nach bestem Gewissen und Geschmack entschieden werden.

Meinem Freund Dr. Ludwig Landshoff in Berlin, dem besten Kenner Joh. Christian Bachs, habe ich für Ratschläge, Mr. F. T. Arnold in London für Durchsicht der englischen Übersetzung schönstens zu danken, auch Prof. Dr. Fr. Noack in Darmstadt bin ich für eine Auskunft sehr verpflichtet.

✳

Unsere Sinfonie ist gewissermaßen eine „französische" Sinfonie (natürlich nichts weniger als eine französische Ouvertüre im eigentlichen Sinn des Wortes), aber eine Sinfonia im französischen Geschmack, ganz ähnlich der für das Concert spirituel im Jahre 1778 von Mozart komponierten, mit der sie auch die Tonart teilt. Auch sie beginnt mit dem „premier coup d'archet", den Johann Christian überhaupt sehr geliebt hat, und steigert ein Allerwelts-Thema ohne viel Verwicklung zum Fortissimo auf der Dominant – es ist, wie wenn ein festliches Portal mit prunkvoller Fröhlichkeit geöffnet würde — die 2. Geigen geben sogar ein paar französische Läufe oder Anläufe dazu. Es erscheint ein zierliches zweites Thema, das mit einer ganz mozartischen Wendung wieder in die Region des Hauptmotivs hineinführt — das nun aber plötzlich seinen Allerwelts-Charakter verliert und seinen tieferen Wert enthüllt. Wir stehen in einer Art von Durchführung, ohne es zu merken, es ist alles von einer erstaunlichen Einheitlichkeit und Abwechslung. Man verlange nur noch keine Haydnsche „diskursive" Auseinandersetzung der Themen; eine Bachsche Sinfonia ist nicht das Hauptstück eines Konzertabends, sondern Eröffnung, Abschluß, Zwischenspiel, sie darf eine bestimmte Grenze des Gefühls und der Betontheit nicht überschreiten. So sind denn auch die Wolkenschatten, die da und dort die pastorale Landschaft des zweiten Satzes verdunkeln, nicht bedrohlich, und ganz

französisch heiter wird es in dem abschließenden Rondo, mit seinen beiden zierlichen „Couplets" und der geistreich zusammenfassenden Coda. Aber im Ganzen: welche Frische der Erfindung, welche Fülle von Witz! Diese Sinfonie war ein Werk für Kenner, für „Connoisseurs". Sie werden es zu würdigen gewußt haben, wenn im Mittelteil des ersten Satzes, den Durchführung zu nennen wir uns nicht getrauten, das cantable Thema nicht schmeichlerisch, sondern laut und Sforzando erscheint; sie werden es genossen haben, wenn in der Reprise der Eintritt des zweiten Themas nicht mehr so glatt erreicht wird wie beim ersten Mal, sondern auf einem ziemlich bedrohlichen Umweg (Takt 104 ff.); das instrumentale Wechselspiel im Crescendo der Coda (Takt 140 ff.) wird ihnen neu und reizvoll erschienen sein. Diese Sinfonie spiegelt von Johann Christian Bachs musikalischer Persönlichkeit nur einen Teil wider: nur seinen Witz, seine Liebenswürdigkeit, seine Heiterkeit, nicht die eigentümliche starke und zarte Sinnlichkeit, die er in Italien in sein Wesen aufgenommen hat. Aber auch in dieser Beschränkung ist sie etwas Gerundetes und Ganzes.

Alfred Einstein

Sinfonia

I

Johann Christian Bach, Op. 18 No. 4
1735 – 1782

E. E. 3693

Ernst Eulenburg Ltd

2

4

6

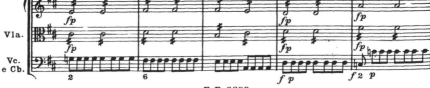

60

8

12

E.E.3693

II

III

Rondo
Presto